PET ALERT

Contents

Jan Burchett
and Sara Vogler

Story illustrated by
Martin Chatterton

Heinemann

D0258287

In this story

 Sami Search

 The neighbour

Tricky words

- neighbour
- built
- investigate
- strange
- terrible
- clues
- rescue centre
- mystery

Introduce these tricky words and help the reader when they come across them later!

Story starter

Sami Search wants to be a detective when he grows up. He thinks he is great at solving crimes, but he always gets things wrong. When he sees strange boxes in a neighbour's garden, Sami Search investigates. Let him tell you about his latest case.

The Case
of the
Petnapper

A new neighbour came to live next door to me. She built lots of sheds in her garden. What did she want all those sheds for?

Then one day I saw some boxes
in my neighbour's garden –
big boxes and small boxes. What
did she want all those boxes for?

I had to investigate.

"This is a case for me," I said.

I got out my notebook.

I waited until there was no one
around. I looked over the fence.
I could see the boxes.
There were strange noises
coming from the boxes, and then
one of them moved!

I checked that no one could see me
and I climbed over the fence.
I crept up to the boxes.
They were full of animals!
All different kinds of animals.

Why do you think
the neighbour is
keeping all those
animals?

I had to find out why my neighbour had all those animals.

Then I had a terrible thought.

I hadn't seen my cat Fluffy all day.

Where could she be?

I wrote down all the clues in my notebook:

- The garden is full of sheds and boxes.
- The sheds and boxes are full of animals.
- Fluffy is missing.

Then I knew what my neighbour was doing.
She was a petnapper!

I had to rescue Fluffy and all the animals. But how?

I had an idea.

I went home and got some pet food.

I climbed back over the fence.
I opened all the boxes. All the
animals ran to the pet food.

The animals were pleased to be free.

They climbed all over me.

But I still couldn't see Fluffy.

Then my neighbour came back.
"What do you think you are
doing?" she said.
"I am saving the animals," I said.
"You are a petnapper!"

"I am not a petnapper," she said.

"I run a pet rescue centre."

Then I saw Fluffy on the fence.

Had she been there all this time?

I helped my neighbour put the animals back into the boxes.
Then I got out my notebook.
"Another mystery solved," I said.
"Case closed!"

Text Detective

- Why did Sami think his neighbour was a petnapper?
- Would you have investigated the strange boxes?

Word Detective

- **Phonic Focus:** Long vowel phonemes
  Page 11: Sound out the three phonemes in 'home'. What long vowel phoneme can you hear?
- Page 11: Find a word meaning 'save'.
- Page 12: Find two past tense verbs ending 'ed'.

Super Speller

Read these words:

climbed   missing   waited

Now try to spell them!

HA! HA! HA!

Q What pets make cool music?

A Trum-pets!

Before Reading

Find out about

- Some unusual things that pets can do

Tricky words

- unusual
- tightrope
- owners
- shower
- skateboarding
- rescued
- water skiing

Introduce these tricky words and help the reader when they come across them later!

Text starter

Animals do not always behave in the way we think they will. Sometimes pets like to copy people. These pets have learned to do some very unusual things – like Zoe the cat, who can walk on a tightrope!

Wacky Animals

Zoe is a very unusual cat.

She can do a very unusual trick.

She can walk on a tightrope!

Most cats do not like water, but Ice Breaker does like water. His owners were surprised to see him swimming in the pool.

Now Ice Breaker likes to surf at the beach.
He likes the water so much he even takes a shower!

Do you think it is easier to surf with four legs?

Snowy is a very unusual dog.
She saw children skateboarding and
she jumped on the board and went
down the slope!

Now she likes skateboarding so much that she even uses her back paws to make the skateboard go faster. She has her own skateboard and likes to ride it every day.

Dinky the dingo was found in a trap
when he was a puppy.
A man rescued him and took him
home.

A dingo is a wild
dog in Australia.

Dinky likes to sing. He is a very
good singer – for a dingo!
Lots of people come to hear him.

Momoko is a very unusual monkey.
Her owners have a boat and they
like to go water skiing.
Now Momoko goes water skiing
with the family.

She can water ski at 20mph.
That is faster than most
people can water ski.
She even likes skiing on snow!

Bert the camel lives in America.
Bert has a very unusual job.
He works for the police.

But Bert does not catch robbers. His job is to go to schools with his trainer. The children learn how the police used camels long ago.

Parts of America are like a desert, so the police once used camels!

Ara is a very unusual parrot.

She likes to skate!

First she learned to skate on

roller-skates but now she can

skate on ice.

Hotshot is a very unusual horse.
He likes to go on a see-saw. Hotshot
nods his head to make the see-saw
go up and down.

Quiz

Text Detective

- Which animal do you think is the most unusual?
- Do you know any animals that can do tricks?

Word Detective

- Phonic Focus: Long vowel phonemes
  Page 30: Sound out the four phonemes in 'skate'.
  What long vowel phoneme can you hear?
- Page 22: Find a word meaning the opposite of 'usual'.
- Page 23: Find a word with three syllables.

Super Speller

Read these words:

goes   first   ride

Now try to spell them!

HA! HA! HA!

Q How do you stop a dog digging up your garden?

A Take away his spade!